© SUSAETA EDICIONES, S.A.
Editor in Chief: Ana Doblado
Original Spanish Text: A-rredondo / Susaeta editorial team
Book Design and Illustrations: A-rredondo
Production: Antonia Maria Martinez
Art Editor: José de Haro

ISBN: 978-0-7097-1777-5
© 2007 Brown Watson, English Edition
Reprinted 2008

Design and illustrations
A-rredondo

English edition translated from
the Spanish and edited by
Maureen Spurgeon

Under the Sea

Brown Watson

Mountain waters

The lives of so many animals depend on the waters flowing through mountain rivers and streams – not only fish, but also amphibians (creatures which live on land and in water), reptiles, beavers, otters, bears and a huge variety of other creatures who get their food from water.

On this page, there is one prehistoric animal, and two from Africa. Can you find them all?

The Grizzly Bear is very clever at fishing for trout and salmon! Find 11 Grizzly Bears!

When it senses danger, a beaver thumps the water with its tail. Find 11 beavers.

Otters round up their prey in shallow waters before they begin hunting it down. Can you see 8 otters?

When trout leap up in the waters of a river, they make a great feast for the Grizzly Bear. Very few get away! There are 35 to find, in total.

The Elk is the largest of all deer, growing up to 3 metres. It is also an excellent swimmer. Can you find 12?

In the rivers

If you gaze absently at a river, it might seem that there are no living things in the water. But if you look closer, beneath the surface, between the stones, in the hollows and among the plant-life, you will soon see a vast number of water creatures.

Find 3 animals which do not live in rivers.

There are more than 4,000 species of frogs and toads, many with spectacular colourings. Find 16.

Tadpoles are born without limbs, but these soon grow. Find 14 tadpoles.

The claws of the Fi... Eagle are shaped like litt... pincers - ideal f... grabbing hold of its pre...

Did you know that there is a tiny little frog, the size of your fingernail? It is called the Phyllomedusa. Be careful as you search for 15!

6

A salmon can swim more than 1600 kilometres along a river, leaping and jumping great heights to reach a place for spawning. See if you can find 10.

The kingfisher captures its prey with a snap of its beak. With its bright colours, it will be easy for you to find 7.

In the lakes

Water loses speed in a lake, because of its wide expanse. Not all creatures living in lakes are fish. There are also ducks, swans, geese, herons, and many other birds.

Find four animals which are neither birds nor fish.

Herons are nearly always seen lying in wait for fish – then, when they one ... zap! Can you find 14 among all the birds here?

The swan feeds on wate plants. In spite of its larg size, it migrates at grea heights when winte approache Find 10 swans

A pike can grow up to 1.5 metres. So you should find it easy to spot 12.

There are distinct differences in colouring between male and female ducks. Males tend to be more brightly coloured.
Find 17 ducks.

The Great Crested Grebe rarely flies. On land, it moves slowly. But in the water, it is a great diver.
Find 10.

In marshy waters

Many animals live in the swamps and marshes throughout the world. Some are dangerous, hiding themselves among the plant-life and in the hollows, nooks and crannies and hidden places.
So, take care!

Please rescue 4 farm animals which are in danger!

Shoals of Piranha Fish can devour a large animal within a short time. Find 23, but don't get too close!

Snakes slither silently among the branches of trees. Can you discover 10?

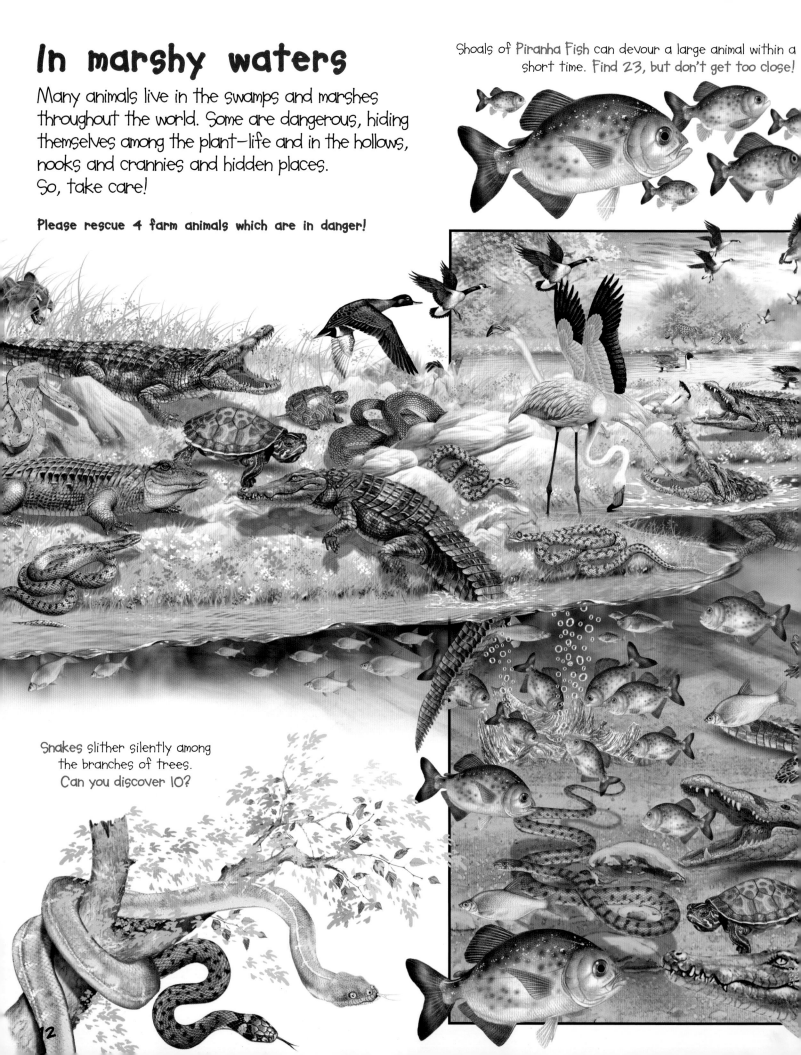

Crocodiles and caimans are the most powerful creatures living in jungle swamps. They are feared by all other animals, except human beings. Before they open their mouths too wide, can you find 16 adults and 4 young?

Weighed down by their hard shells, turtles cannot help making a good meal sometimes! Can you find 12, before they get eaten?

13

Coral seas

Coral reefs are like enormous gardens beneath the sea, home to a huge variety of fish. Some of these are very beautiful, with spectacular colouring. Others are fierce and aggressive, like the shark.

Can you see 3 animals which do not belong here?

The Clown Fish has the disadvantage of looking unfriendly to its companions! Here there are 5 to find.

The Manta Ray is the largest of all ray fish, showing the point of its fins outside the water when it sunbathes. You can see this by finding 6.

The largest turtle in existence is the Leatherback Sea Turtle, which can weigh up to 600 kilograms. Can you see 10?

The Barracuda is a fierce species of fish. It can attack a person if it is disturbed. Can you see 6?

This fish is called the **Parrot Fish** because its mouth is like a parrot's bill. It uses this to tear apart pieces of hard coral. Can you find 6 Parrot Fish?

There are about a hundred different species of surgeon fish, all in the most beautiful colours. Find 3 surgeon fish of each colour.

The most frightening

In the seas there are many creatures which people have long feared — some because of their great appetite for food, others for their dangerous bites which can often be poisonous. In most cases, there are remedies ... except for the bite of the shark.

Among all these dangerous animals, there are 3 which would never go near the sea. Which are they?

The **White Shark** is the largest shark of all, weighing many tonnes and reaching lengths of up to 13 metres. Take care when you go hunting for 7!

The **Saw Fish** lives in the deepest coast waters and uses its 'saw' to remov sand in search of food. Can you find 5

A **Jellyfish** is transparent and gelatinous. 95% of its weight is water, and it is armed with stinging tentacles. Can you find 7 jellyfish without getting stung?

The **Scorpion Fish** is highly poisonous — it can even kill a human being. Find 7 — but take care!

The **Moray Eel** can give some dangerous bites with its sharp teeth if it is disturbed. Don't you disturb any, when you search for 9!

The Swordfish is a rapid hunter, feeding on small fish and cuttlefish and not letting any escape. You will need no prodding to find 5!

The Hammerhead Shark gets its name because of the flat shapes at either side of its head, making it look like a hammer. Can you see where its eyes are? Now open your eyes and find 4!

Flying or swimming?

It seems normal to think of fish being under the water. But we shall see from rock to see the jumps of almost a hundred metres distance and various metres in height which some fish can reach.

Amid so much flight, it is not difficult to see 4 turtles!

The dolphin is the most playful and the most intelligent of all sea mammals, often making the most spectacular leaps above the water.
You will jump for joy if you can find 13!

The Flying Fish can move quickly a water with jumps of more 90 metres in the See if you can fir

The Sperm Whale can remain submerged at depths of more than 1000 metres, hunting for Giant Squid.
Stay on the surface and find 6!

The Blue Whale is the largest mammal to have ever existed. It can grow to 30 metres in length and weigh 140 tonnes. See if you can find just 7.

The Giant Squid lives at depths of more than 1000 metres, and grows up to 20 metres. It often gets involved in fierce battles with sperm whales. Can you see 10?

The Sail Fish flies up from the water at a speed of 100 kilometres an hour! It is the fastest of all fish. Run and find 10!

Animals at the Poles

And so we come to the Poles, the Arctic and the Antarctic, to see some of the creatures who live near the water, at the coldest places on Earth.

There are 3 animals here who would not survive in such cold surroundings. Which are they?

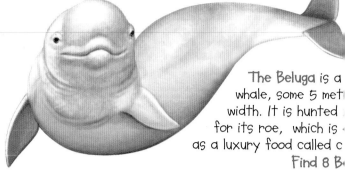

The Beluga is a whale, some 5 met width. It is hunted for its roe, which is as a luxury food called c
Find 8 B

Seal pups can swim only a few hours after birth – and after two or three days, they can dive for up to two minutes. Find 15 seals and pups.

Did you know that the horn of a narwhal is in fact a tooth? It grows through a hole in its upper lip and can reach a length of 2.7 metres. Can you find 8 narwhal?

The male Booby Penguin has tufts of golden feathers on its head, which it shakes to attract a female during mating time. Find 9.

The one egg laid by the female Emperor Penguin is hatched by the male beneath its feet. Hundreds of male Emperor Penguins gather together for warmth. Do not shiver, but find 35!

The walrus, the Marine Elephant and the Sea Lion are all pinnipeds (aquatic mammals). Find 5 of each.

The most fantastic

It is impossible to show the vast number of fantastic animals which exist in all the oceans, seas, lakes and rivers of the world – but here we shall see some of the most amazing.

Crabs are not all that fantastic – but you can find 3.

The skin of the Stone F[ish] looks almost invisible again[st] the rocks. See if y[ou] can find

This may not look like it – but this is a sea horse. Its seaweed-like fins are a good means of camouflage. Find 4.

The Sprocket Wheel Fish inflates itself by taking in water, in order to defend itself against its enemies. If you take care, you can find 7.

The Moon Fish gives the impression of being only a very large head! Don't lose your head – find 6 Moon Fish!

The Trunkfish is the slowest and hardest of all fish, due to the bony structure of its skeleton. Find 4 of each colour.

The 'false eye' of the Butterfly Fish confuses its enemies! Don't you be confused when you search for 6!

In search of treasure

The seas of our planet offer us a rich supply of resources – not just food, but also sunken treasure, minerals, oil and natural gas. But, if we keep using up its stocks without giving the sea a chance to recover, in time there will be very little left.

Among all this sunken treasure, from many years ago, there are 4 modern objects wich do not belong.

In olden days, coins were made of precious metals, such as gold and silver. See if you can find 9 coins

Frogmen descend to great depths, searching among sunken ships. Dive down and see if you can find 10 frogmen.

Pirates plundered ships, stealing chests of gold and jewels. No need for you to steal – there are 7 treasure chests to find.

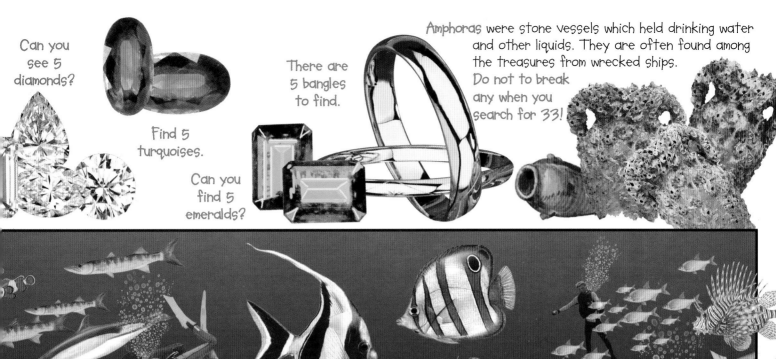

Can you see 5 diamonds?

Find 5 turquoises.

Can you find 5 emeralds?

There are 5 bangles to find.

Amphoras were stone vessels which held drinking water and other liquids. They are often found among the treasures from wrecked ships. Do not to break any when you search for 33!

The deepest depths

At more than 4000 metres below the surface of the sea, there is an incredible community of fish. Some shine like torches and lanterns. Others beam like underwater lighthouses. There are also many rare sea creatures, some very small and totally blind, yet shining in the darkness.

In the darkness, can you see 4 cans of drink?

The Tripod Fish rests on three fins on the sea bed.

The Hatchet Fish has many luminous organs. At night-time, it swims to the surface to eat. Find 3.

With the trail of light coming from the Lantern Fish, it should be easy for you to find 22.

he Fangtooth (or Ogrefish)
es its luminous antenna to
tract its prey, and then
apture it. Don't
u be dazzled!
nd 10!

With its wide, luminous antenna, the Pacific
Viperfish draws its victims towards its mouth.
Don't be confused by its
light when you look for 12.

27

Pollution of the sea

Everything ends up in the sea – pollution of the air, the land, and the sea itself, as well as pesticides used in farming, the aftermath of fires and explosions, disasters on oil rigs, rubbish dumped into the sea, chemicals, plastics and acid rain.

Can you find 3 old shoes among all the rubbish?

Nuclear power is the cheapest but also the most dangerous method of producing energy. Cross out 4 nuclear power stations.

Plastic rings from cans of drink and pieces of fishing nets pose a great danger to dolphins. Can you help by finding 8 cans?

Birds are the main victims of oil slicks on the sea, when oil floats towards the coast. See if you can rescue 10 birds.

Nuclear waste is put into **barrels** which are then dumped on sea beds. Reclaim 24 barrels.